THE PIANO TRANSCRIPTIONS

RAY CHARLES

Hal•Leonard®

Published by
Hal Leonard

Exclusive distributors:

Hal Leonard
7777 West Bluemound Road
Milwaukee, WI 53213
Email: info@halleonard.com

Hal Leonard Europe Limited
42 Wigmore Street
Marylebone, London, W1U 2RN
Email: info@halleonardeurope.com

Hal Leonard Australia Pty. Ltd.
4 Lentara Court
Cheltenham, Victoria, 3192 Australia
Email: info@halleonard.com.au

Order No. AM92019
ISBN 0-7119-4126-2

Music arranged by Paul Honey and Camden Music.
Music processed by Paul Ewers Music Design and Camden Music.
Compiled by Nick Crispin.
Cover photograph courtesy of LFI.

www.halleonard.com

DROWN IN MY OWN TEARS 5

GEORGIA ON MY MIND 10

HALLELUJAH I LOVE HER SO 22

HARD TIMES (NO ONE KNOWS BETTER THAN I) 15

I BELIEVE TO MY SOUL 28

I CAN'T STOP LOVING YOU 34

LET'S GO GET STONED 40

LONELY AVENUE 46

SHAKE A TAIL FEATHER 52

A SONG FOR YOU 59

STICKS AND STONES 92

TAKE THESE CHAINS FROM MY HEART 66

UNCHAIN MY HEART 72

WHAT'D I SAY 78

DROWN IN MY OWN TEARS

WORDS & MUSIC BY HENRY GLOVER

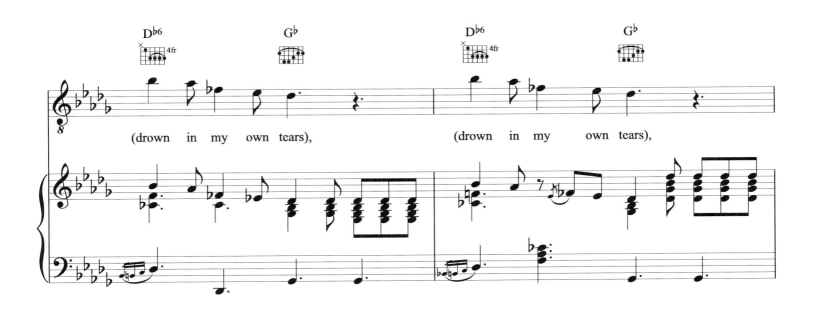

(drown in my own tears), (drown in my own tears),

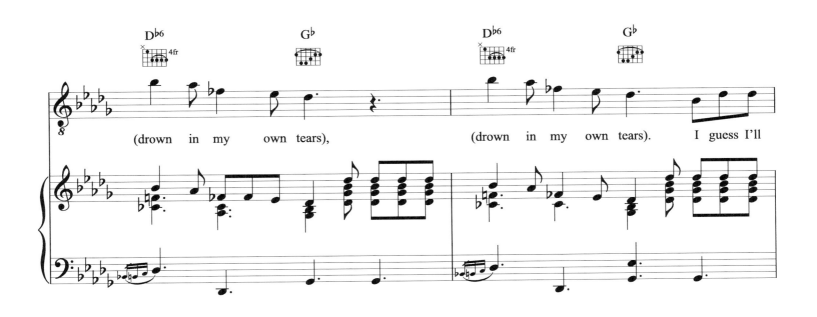

(drown in my own tears), (drown in my own tears). I guess I'll

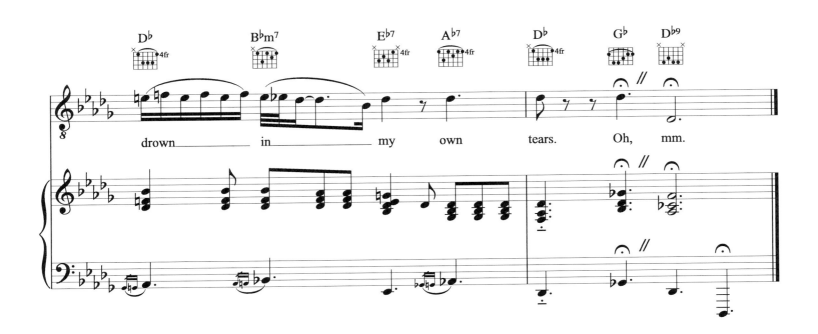

drown_____ in_____ my own tears. Oh, mm.

GEORGIA ON MY MIND

WORDS BY STUART GORRELL
MUSIC BY HOAGY CARMICHAEL

HARD TIMES (NO ONE KNOWS BETTER THAN I)

WORDS & MUSIC BY RAY CHARLES

those hard___ times. Whoah, yeah._____ Who knows___ bet-ter than I?"___

Well I soon found___ out

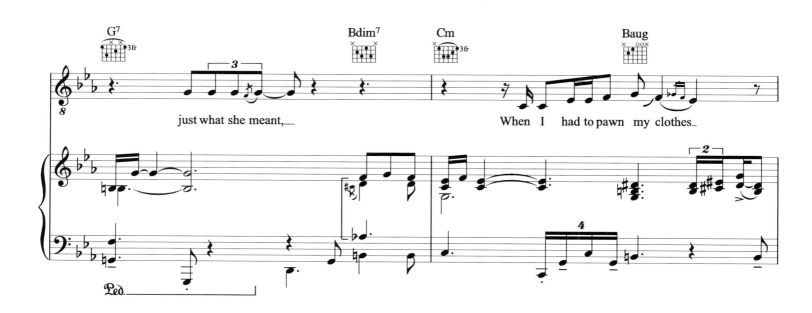

just what she meant,___ When I had to pawn my clothes___

just to pay my rent. Talk-in' 'bout hard_____ times, hard_

____ times._____ Whoah, yeah._____ Who knows a-well a bet-ter than I?_

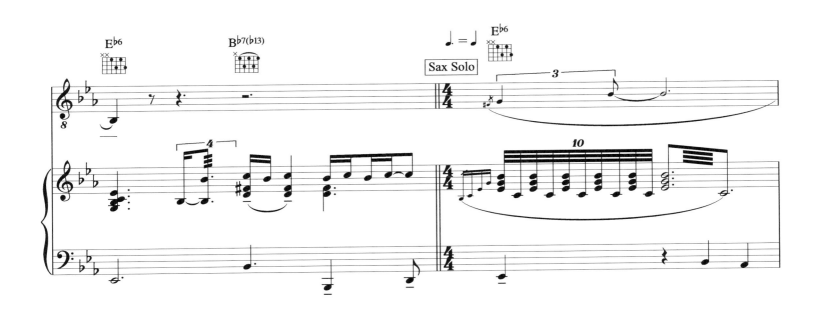

17

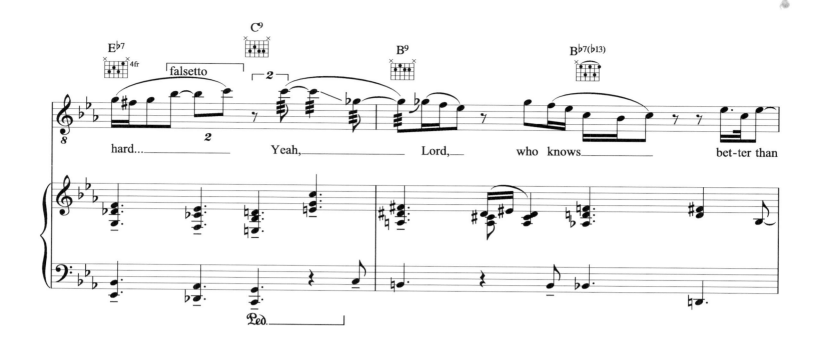

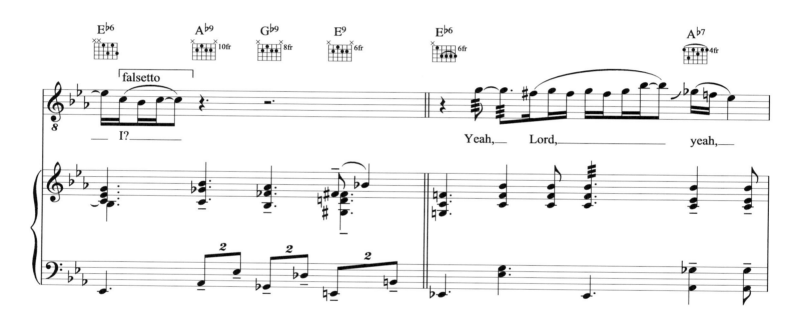

HALLELUJAH I LOVE HER SO

WORDS & MUSIC BY RAY CHARLES

More swing feel

Let me tell you 'bout a girl I know,— she is my ba-by and she

and tell me Dad-dy ev-'ry-thing's all right. That's why I know,_____ yes_____

_____ I know, hal-le-lu-jah I just love her so.

Sax. solo

27

I BELIEVE TO MY SOUL

WORDS & MUSIC BY RAY CHARLES

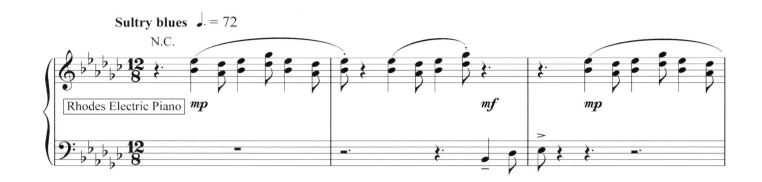

I CAN'T STOP LOVING YOU

WORDS & MUSIC BY DON GIBSON

go,_____ still make me blue. They say___ that

time heals a bro - ken heart, but time has stood

still since we've been a - part. I can't stop

lov - ing you), I said I've made up my mind_____

LET'S GO GET STONED

WORDS & MUSIC BY NICKOLAS ASHFORD, VALERIE SIMPSON & JOSEPHINE ARMSTEAD

LONELY AVENUE

WORDS & MUSIC BY DOC POMUS

die, I could die, I could die, 'cos I live on a lone - ly av - e - nue,

lone - ly av - e - nue.

Sax Solo

(Ah,

SHAKE A TAIL FEATHER

WORDS & MUSIC BY OTIS HAYES, ANDRE WILLIAMS & VERLIE RICE

why didn't you ask___ me ba - by, or did - n't you think___ I could?___

___ Well I know___ that the Boo - gi - loo is out of sight, but the

Shing - a - ling's the thing to - night, but if that were you and me out now ba -

- by I would have shown you how to do it right,___ do it right,___

do it right,_____ do it right,__

do it right,___ do it right.___

Aah._____

gliss.

D   G⁷   D

Twist - in'   shake it, shake it, shake it, shake it,   ba - by,_____

mf cresc.

58

A SONG FOR YOU

WORDS & MUSIC BY LEON RUSSELL

I've been so many places in my life and time.

I've sung a lot of songs, I've made some bad rhymes.

But now I'm__ so much bet-ter   so if my words   don't__ come to-geth-er,_____

lis-ten to the me-lo-dy   'cos my love's_____ in there hid-ing._____

I   love you in   a   place   where there's no   space   or   time,__

TAKE THESE CHAINS FROM MY HEART

WORDS & MUSIC BY FRED ROSE & HY HEATH

see. Just a_____ spark_____ of the

love that____ used to be._____ If you____

love some-bo-dy new,____ let me____ find a new love

too, take these chains from my heart____ and__ set me free.__

68

UNCHAIN MY HEART

WORDS & MUSIC BY BOBBY SHARP & TEDDY POWELL

Original key A♭ minor

♩ = 154

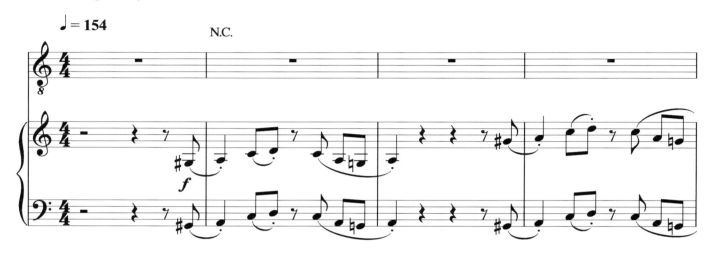

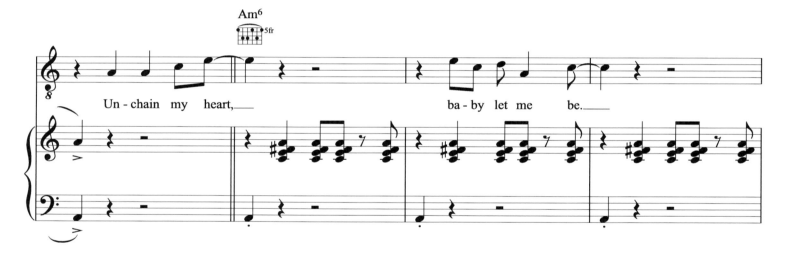

Un-chain my heart,___ ba-by let me be.___

Un-chain my heart,___ 'cos you don't care a-bout me.

'cos you don't love me no more.

Ev - 'ry time I call you on the phone,

some fel - la tells me that you're not at home, so un-chain my heart, oh

please, please set me free. I'm un - der your spell

WHAT'D I SAY

WORDS & MUSIC BY RAY CHARLES

al - right,

al - right.

When you see me in mi-se-ry, come on ba-by see a-bout me now, yeah,

Hey, hey, al-

-right.

See the girl with the red dress on, she can do the Bird-land all night long,

86

Said a-one more time,___ ba-by now,
Make me feel so good___ now,___ yeah.
said that it's al-right___ right___ now,

said a-one more time___ now,___
Woah,___ Ba-by,___
said___ it's al-right,___

said a-one more time,___
make me feel so good___
said___ it's al-right___

___ yeah.
___ yeah.
___ yeah.

Said a-one more time,___
Make me feel so good,___
Said___ it's al-right,___

STICKS AND STONES
WORDS & MUSIC BY TITUS TURNER

Peo-ple talk-in' tryin' to break us up, { yeah; 𝄋: and they } scan-dal-i-zin' my name.___ They'll

say an-y-thing___ just to make me feel bad,___ yes an-y-thing to make me shame.___

Piano Solo